GREAT CARTOONS OF THE WORLD

GREAT CARTOONS OF THE WORLD

BY THE WORLD'S FOREMOST CARTOONISTS
THIRD SERIES

EDITED BY JOHN BAILEY

CROWN PUBLISHERS, INC., NEW YORK

Acknowledgments and thanks are gratefully
made to the following publishers and cartoonists
for permitting the use of the cartoons appearing in this book:

THE PUBLISHERS:

Bärmeier & Nikel, Dikobraz, Editions Denoël, Harper & Row, Look, Nebelspalter,
Saturday Review, The New Yorker, The Saturday Evening Post, This Week, Paris Match,
Punch, United Feature Syndicate

THE CARTOONISTS:

Charles Addams, Ed Arno, Miroslav Bartak, Quentin Blake, Bosc, Mel Calman, Cesc,
Whitney Darrow, Jr., Chon Day, Robert Day, Eldon Dedini, Boris Drucker,
Stanislav Duda, Volker Ernsting, Michael ffolkes, John Glashan, Harry Hargreaves,
Syd Hoff, Stanislav Holý, Stan Hunt, Edward Koren, Anatol Kovarsky, Lee Lorenz,
Charles Martin, Frank Modell, Guillermo Mordillo, Hans Moser, Tony Munzlinger,
Lou Myers, William O'Brian, Terence Parkes, Virgil Partch, Bruce Petty, George Price,
Donald Reilly, Vladimir Renčin, Mischa Richter, Charles Saxon, Charles Schulz,
Jean-Jacques Sempé, A. G. Sens, Vahan Shirvanian, Fredy Sigg, Claude Smith,
Ton Smits, Leslie Starke, Jules Stauber, William Steig, James Stevenson,
Henry Syverson, Bill Tidy, Barney Tobey, Robert Weber

© 1969, by Crown Publishers, Inc.
Library of Congress Catalog Card Number: 67-27025
Printed in the U.S.A.
Published simultaneously in Canada by General Publishing Company Limited

Jacket design and layout by Laura Jean Allen

ust as the easel-painter directs the eye with the use of color, so the cartoonist directs the eye with the use of line. In a painting of a landscape, the blues recede into the distance, the trees are coolly green, and suddenly Corot puts a spot of red on a figure—a farmhand's shirt, or a woman's skirt—directing the eye to a center of interest. The cartoonist achieves the same result with a spot of black—a black necktie on the person speaking, for instance—and lines lead you subtly to the thing he would like you to see second, just as Corot used drooping tree limbs to guide your eye down to a figure. Rouault put heavy lines around the main features of his paintings to compel the eye, and cartoonists do the same thing. The spot of red or black attracts the eye in the same way as does a single blonde in a chorus of black-haired women. Indeed, the art of the cinema follows the same rules, and a good director leads your eye to the person speaking by using the same devices and, like the easel-painter and the cartoonist, sees to it that there is no one in the background leaping around in a red suit to distract the eye. In the Sempé drawing of the life preserver, it is not an accident that your eye goes first to the running man, second to the drowning man, and third to the box the life preserver is kept in.

All right-thinking people agree that Steig is a genius. He is a shrewd and penetrating student of human nature, a profound philosopher, and a great playwright—for many of his things, like Thurber's, could be staged. He sees the whole picture of life, and both animals and humans are subject to Steig's laws and observations. He carries honesty to an extreme. His work is completely genuine, unpretentious, and consistent. There is no such thing as a substandard Steig. His work is timeless, yet ever-changing and evolving.

Saxon, like Steig, represents the true, and perhaps final, flowering of American cartooning, which with them has been raised to a very high level. Saxon has done for this generation what Cruikshank and Hogarth did for theirs. He is a social historian—and whereas Steig's drawings are timeless, Saxon has to do with what's going on now. In particular he has concentrated on the crowd that travels, eats well, drinks well, says certain things, and does certain things. He understands how the modern body moves in its clothes, and eats, drinks, and stands. He reports all this in drawings of great style and mastery of form, not literally, but with subtle caricature, and without Daumier's anger.

If one should speak of Whitney Darrow, Jr., as a painter, one would say that he is a traditionalist. His rich tone creates an atmosphere of reality, and tone is an integral part of his thinking. His strong personality and powerful concepts reflect the times as they are, and he combines tradition and modernity in a wonderful way. His subject matter is contemporary but his work is ageless, and put down in any century he would do a perfect job of portraying the times and the people. Furthermore, he possesses a priceless asset rare even among cartoonists—he never fails to be funny.

The powerful, slashing black line of Mischa Richter is as dramatic as if drawn with a stiletto, and his cartoons are composed with the same drama. His technique never gets in the way of what he has to say, as with a deadly wit—and a somewhat cynical view of life—he goes to the heart of hypocrisy. When he chooses to use tone, his drawings are softened a bit, but his view of life does not change.

One can never get enough of Charles Addams' work. He is truly creative and unique, and the inside of his mind must be a wonderful place, full of creepy, crawly things. His Transylvanian imagination has created all sorts of characters, as well as the marvelous, rich world they inhabit, and when he turns them out of that world and into yours, it is very disconcerting. He gives the enjoyment of fantasy, permitting one to be a child and to be scared and to enjoy it.

Barney Tobey is a realist, and at home in reality. His fine, deft drawings are truthful, honest reporting. He sees humor in the commonplace, takes you to the scene, and tells you honestly, and with irony, what happened.

Bosc deals with all of the dreary commonplaces of life, which most people avoid even discussing because they are so dull. He lures the reader into such a boring situation, and just as the tedium is becoming unbearable, he reveals that beneath the gray, dreary existence of his nameless, faceless robots there lurks explosive drama, which Bosc makes absolutely hilarious through the simple but difficult trick of exposing the bald, naked truth. His fresh, inventive mind is as objective as a surgeon's, as with wisdom and extreme clarity he comments on human emotions and the rudeness with which they are treated.

The cartoons of Virgil Partch always convey a feeling of complete freedom. He has his own highly personalized sense of the absurd and the macabre, which is so outrageous that one is simply shocked into laughter. Both his characters and ideas are brilliantly bizarre, and he has created a bizarre style of drawing to fit them.

Robert Weber does precisely what a cartoonist is supposed to do—be funny. He has a very special beat all his own, which is to look with great insight into various occupations. He sees truly and puts the right actors on the right stage. His vigorous drawings have a velvety tone, as if he were drawing with black marshmallows, and they have a deceptively free look. He has a keen eye for weaknesses—the lapse, the lie, the stupidity—and like a human lie-detector he easily exposes flawed thinking and flawed statements.

Stanislav Holý is a Czechoslovakian comic-artist, from which appellation the word "artist," cannot be taken away. He has a deep understanding of form, and so can make fun of it. The richness of suggested detail in his work is satisfying and amusing, and because he possesses a strong sense of design, all the queer things he drags into his drawings work for him. His Kafka-like statements are eternal and transcend a momentary funny thought.

If Paul Klee had followed his early inclination to become a cartoonist, my own idea is that his cartoons would have come very close to those of Quentin Blake. They have a delightful, cheery quality and, though satirical, are involved with the happy world. His crisp line and unplanned, unclichéd kind of drawing appeal to the child in the adult, which perhaps partly accounts for the popularity of his children's books.

Edward Koren has a complete intellectual comprehension of insanity and releases a schizoid world of surrealistic and nutty happenings that are very convincing. His drawings are deceptively crude and primitive, as if a very good draftsman had drawn them with his left hand. This enhances the feeling of insanity, and his disregard for polished draftsmanship and execution is a wonderful relief from the academic. But while there is naïveté in the drawing, there is none in the thinking.

Lorenz is a keen satirist who has retained in his work many of the early traditions of comic drawing and has skillfully joined them to a completely modern way of looking at things. He is an important link between the historic cartoonist and the new, far-out, Steinbergesque, Picasso-influenced cartoonist.

Volker Ernsting is one of the great European cartoonists whose wonderful sense of the ridiculous is truly cosmopolitan while at the same time it remains Germanic—which is to say that his sense of humor is slightly mordant and leans heavily on incongruity.

Cesc is a Spanish cartoonist with a delightful way of drawing which amounts to calligraphy. He is, incidentally, a master of making the eye go where he wants it to go. Like the artist Morandi, who devoted his whole life to making etchings, drawings, and paintings of nothing but bottles, Cesc, so far, seems perfectly content to express all life through his drawings of beggars. He has drawn thousands and shows not the slightest sign of slowing down.

The work of Lou Myers is a perfect marriage of thinking and drawing. With a frenetic and diabolical power and strength, and using a pen-line like a can of worms, he defines a cruel world, and wrenches an amazing amount of humor from the ideas of Freud, Jung, and Adler.

Drucker begins with really funny ideas, and with a fine sense of elimination shows them in stylized drawings. Charles Martin, with craftsmanlike planning and drawing, suggests much detail with a few lines. Claude's drawings sparkle with a knowledgeable use of tone and are distinguished for his unobtrusive simplification of the keenly observed fashion and furniture of the current scene. George Price's mad pedestrian will make you laugh, and so will Bosc's simple and devastating comment on war. Mordillo deals in the ironies of life, slyly showing his own Mordillo tragic world through funny situations—and Robert Day cleverly shows the use of *misdirection* of the eye in the drawing of the man who arrives home and can't find his wife.

There is, in fact, more to making a cartoon than directing the eye. Someone in artistic circles has been saying, lately, "More is less," and it is true that the easel-painter painting, say, a landscape, generally tries to say as much as he can and to show the subject in all its fullness and detail. To the cartoonist, less is more. The cartoonist extracts the essence of a humorous situation, reduces it to its fundamentals, uses nothing extraneous, and draws with much more economy than the easel-painter because he is expressing an idea, rather than showing what's there. It is his job to caricature the salient points and to carry them beyond the realistic into the humorous. All the cartoonists represented in this book are very good at it.

JOHN BAILEY

New York City, 1969

"Make like you're Socrates."

Michael ffolkes

"You're still tensing that left arm, Henderson."

© 1967 Punch

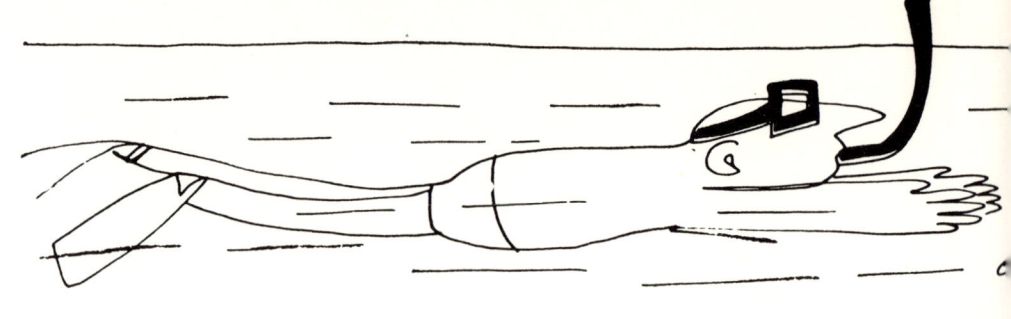

Ed Arno

Vahan Shirvanian "You knew I was bald when you married me." © 1966 The Curtis Publishing Company
Reprinted with permission from THE SATURDAY EVENING POST.

ED. ARNO

© 1965 Look

Boris Drucker

"Ghenghis is hitting me again, Mrs. Khan."

© 1968 Look

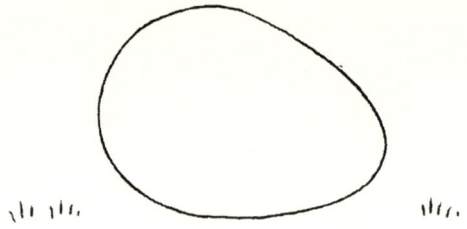
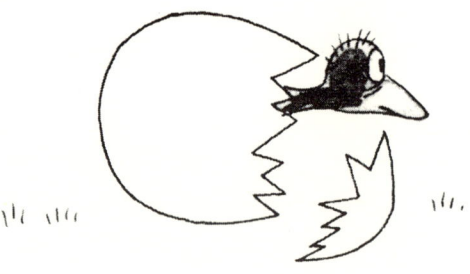

Ton Smits © Ton Smits

Charles Addams "Oh, go to sleep. I'll put up the screens in the morning." Copr. © 1965 The New Yorker Magazine, Inc.

Jean-Jacques Sempé © by Editions Denoël et Sempé

Jules Stauber © Bärmeier & Nikel

Jules Stauber © 1968 Stauber

BOSC

2

4

6

© 1968 Paris Match

John Glashan

© Glashan

Donald Reilly — "Please tell the King I'm sorry." — © 1968 The New Yorker

Stanislav Holy

Robert Weber — "You look great." — Copr. © 1967 The New Yorker Magazine, Inc.

© 1969 Dikobraz

Anatol Kovarsky

© 1969 Kovarsky

"We'd love to have you come for a visit. And bring your little friend with you."

Charles Saxon

Copr. © 1967 The New Yorker Magazine, Inc.

Robert Weber — "You look great." — Copr. © 1967 The New Yorker Magazine, Inc.

Whitney Darrow, Jr.

"We can't go on like this, Miriam. My wife keeps asking me why I don't ever bring the troop home for cocoa and cookies."

Copr. © 1963 The New Yorker Magazine, Inc.

Robert Day — "Be careful what you say. The whole place is bugged."

Syd Hoff   "Yes, you may continue your diet."   © 1969 Look

Leslie Starke   "You are not obliged to say anything unless you wish to do so, but anything you do say will be taken down in writing and may be given in evidence."   © 1963 Punch

Leslie Starke

"You'll have to excuse the mess—
we've got the decorator in."

© Punch

William Steig

"Harry, take it from me. You're doing yourself more harm than good."

Copr. © 1966 The New Yorker Magazine, Inc.

Michael ffolkes

"Looks like another of those wife swapping parties."

"Miss Kent, who took my candy bar?"

Frank Modell

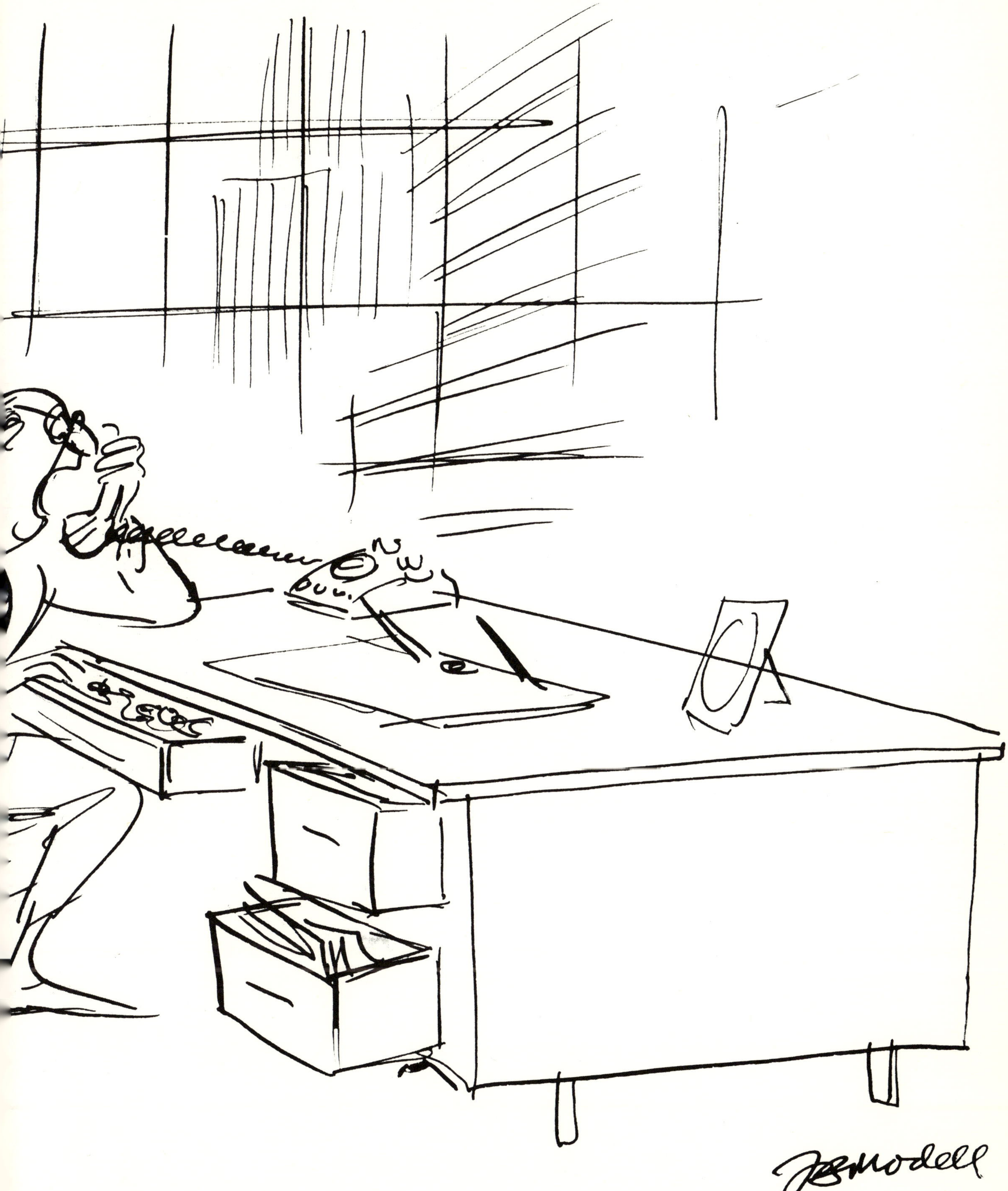

JBModell

Hans Moser

2

4

7

8

© 1968 Nebelspalter

Eldon Dedini

2

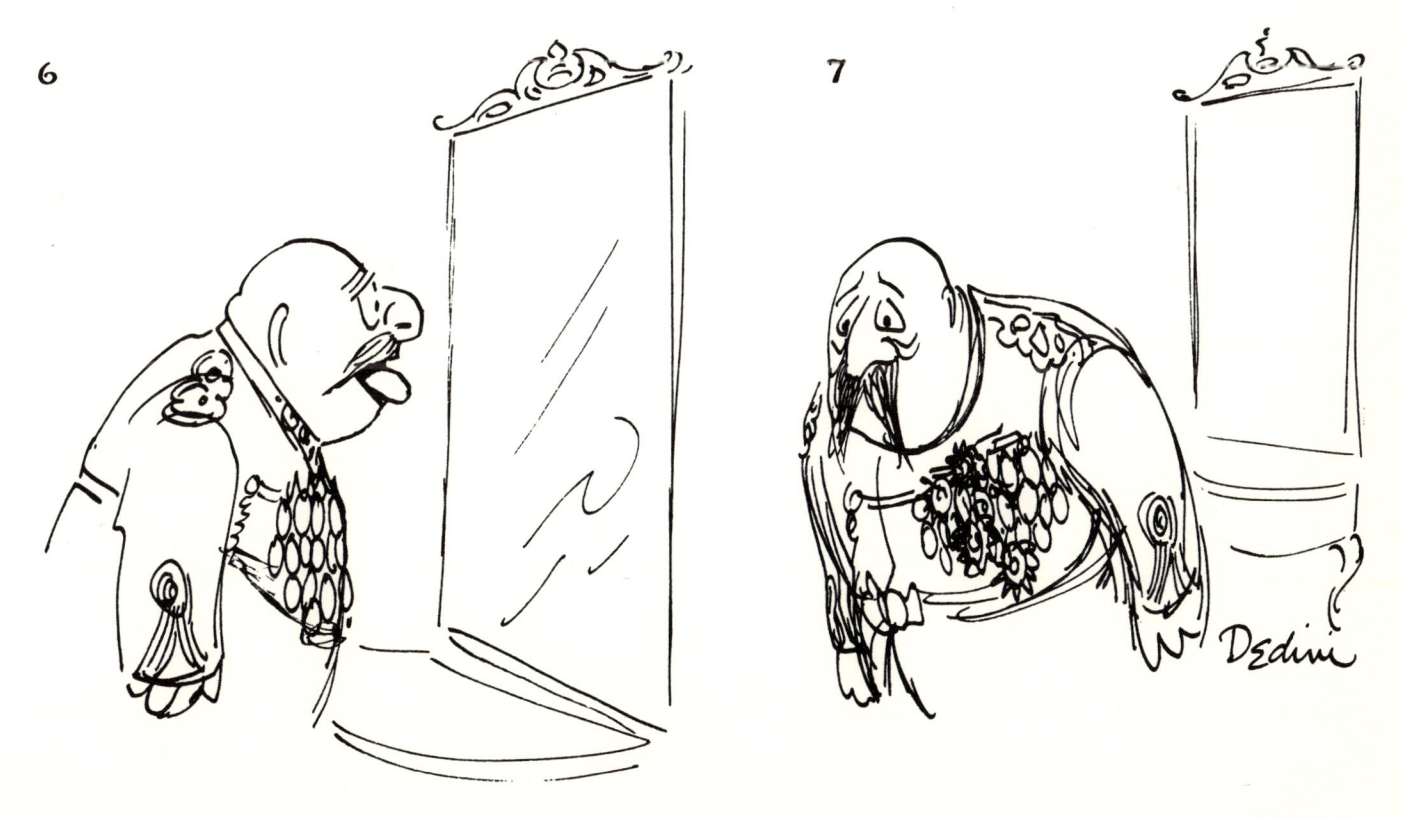

3

6

7

© 1969 Dedini

Guillermo Mordillo

© 1968 Paris Match

Robert Day

"Oh, Linda, I'm home. I'm here. Where are you?"

Miroslav Bartak

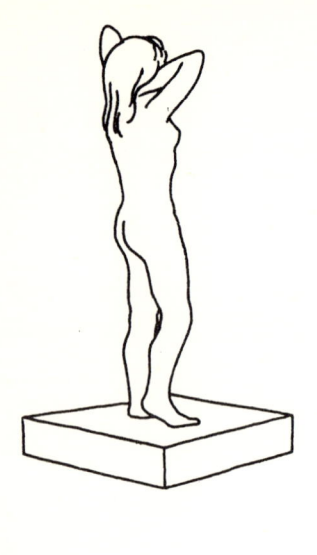

© 1969 Dikobraz

Ton Smits

Tony Munzlinger

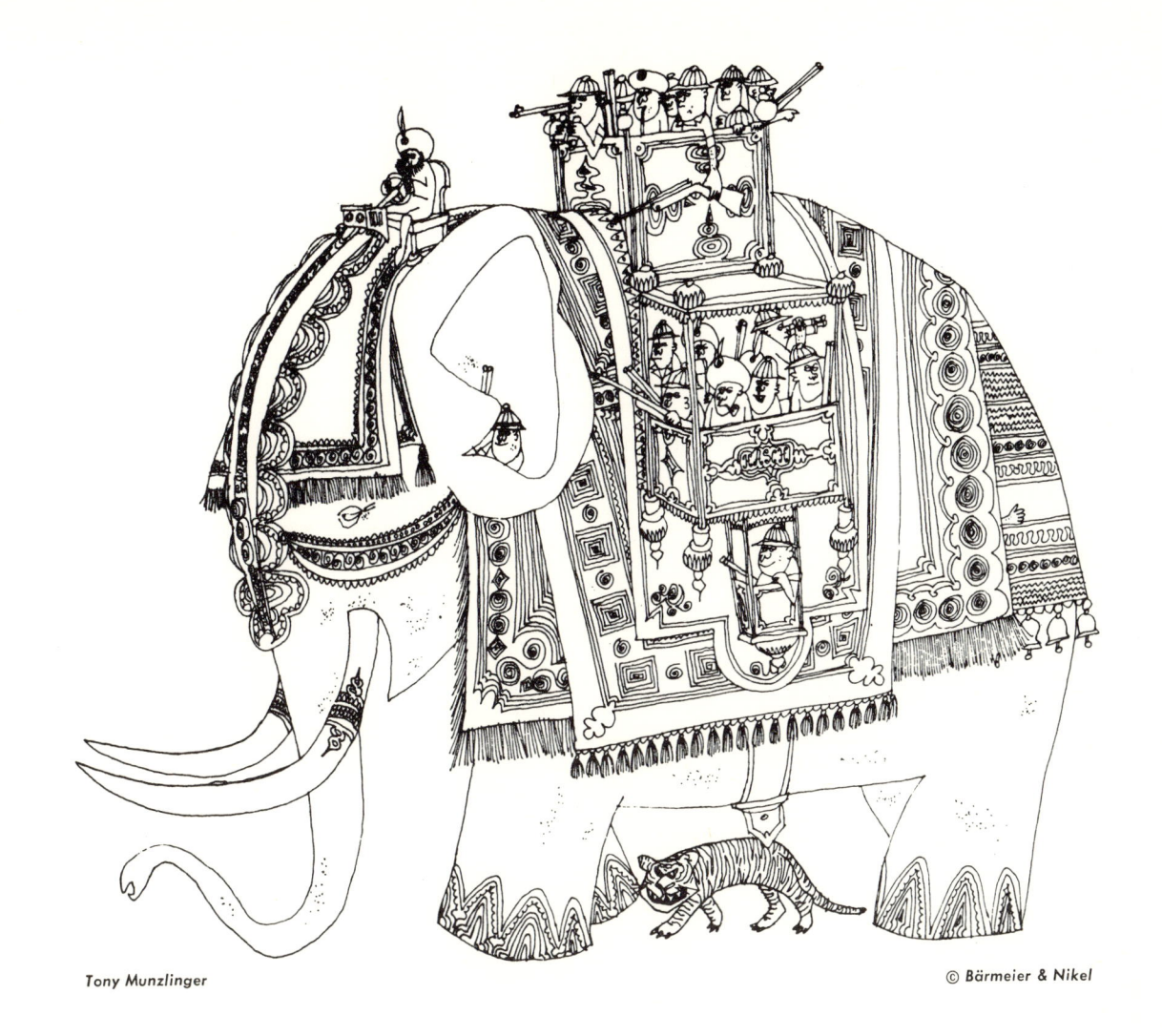

© Bärmeier & Nikel

Copr. © 1966 The New Yorker Magazine, Inc.

Jules Stauber   © 1966 Bärmeier & Nikel

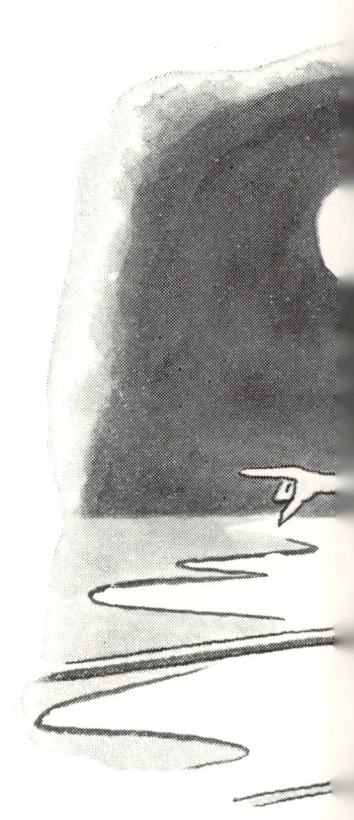

William O'Brian

"Porpoises! Porpoises!"

BOSC

© 1968 Paris Match

Jules Stauber

© 1968 Stauber

Ton Smits

© 1969 Ton Smits

Volker Ernsting

Anatol Kovarsky © 1969 Kovarsky

Guillermo Mordillo © 1968 Paris Match

Anatol Kovarsky

© 1969 Kovarsky

Claude Smith

"He's a little 'in group' all his own."

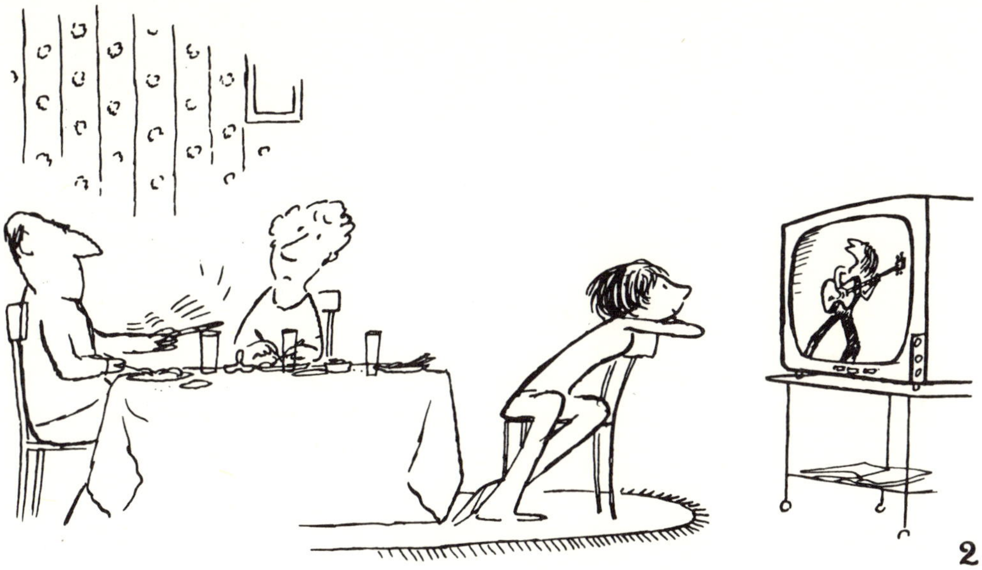

2

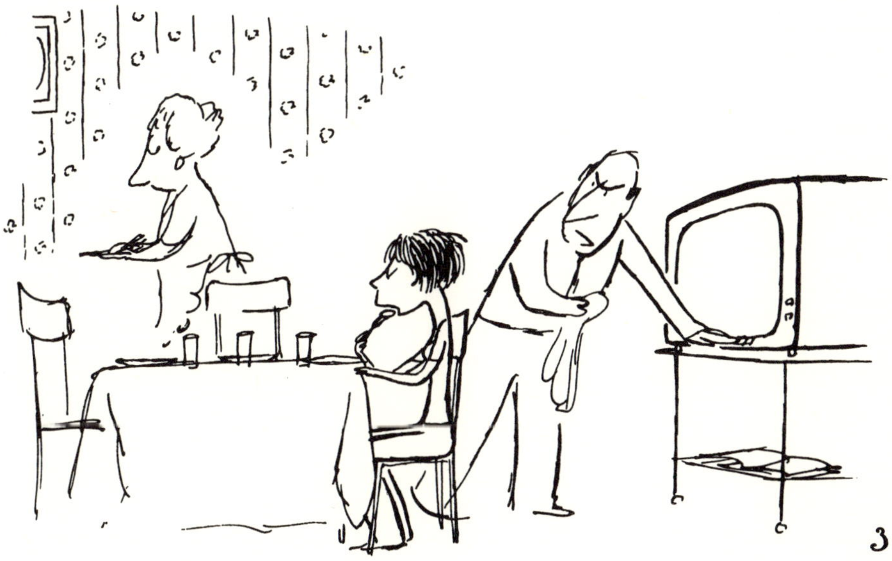

3

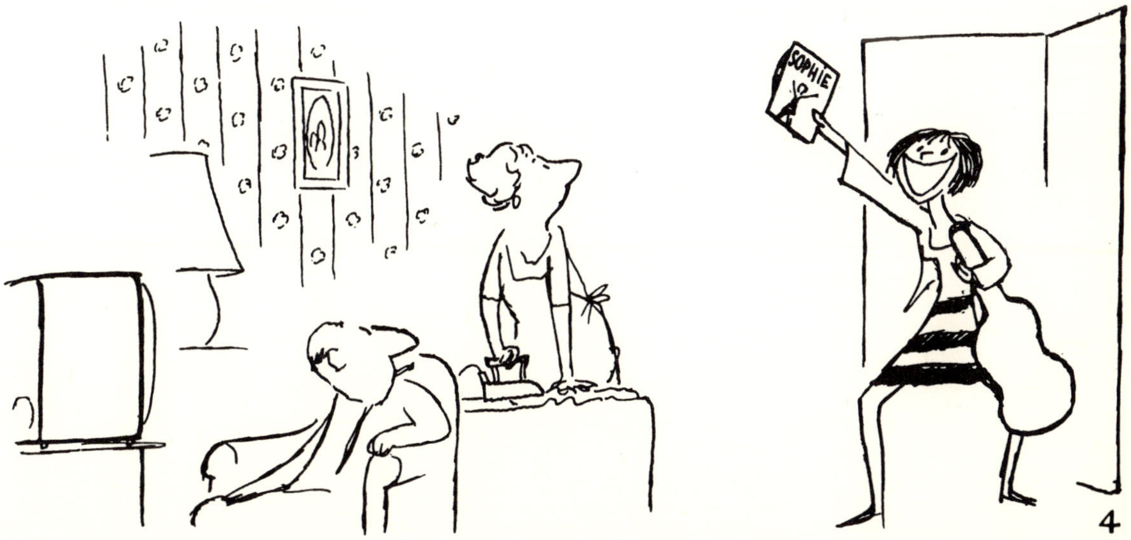

4

5

6

8

7

9

CETTE SEMAINE
LA NOUVELLE IDOLE SOPHIE:
"J'ADORE CHANTER"
ELLE CHANTE (ET COMPOSE) DEPUIS L'ÂGE DE 14 ANS.

10 →

11

13

14

12

15

16

Jean-Jacques Sempé   © by Editions Denoël et Sempé

Vahan Shirvanian

Chon Day "Hold it!" © 1964 The Curtis Publishing Company
Reprinted by permission from THE SATURDAY EVENING POST.

© 1966 The Curtis Publishing Company
Reprinted with permission from THE SATURDAY EVENING POST.

Edward Koren "Talk, talk, talk!" Copr. © 1966 The New Yorker Magazine, Inc.

Fredy Sigg

© Fredy Sigg

Boris Drucker

"We come to your galaxy in peace, with our lasers set on 'simmer.'"

© 1969 Boris Drucker

Charles Martin — "I don't know what it is. I shot it on the way back from a cocktail party in Nairobi." — © 1969 Look

Jules Stauber © Bärmeier & Nikel

Bruce Petty "Not yet! Not yet!" Copr. © 1964 The New Yorker Magazine, Inc.

Cesc

© 1969 Cesc

Bruce Petty

© 1965 Punch

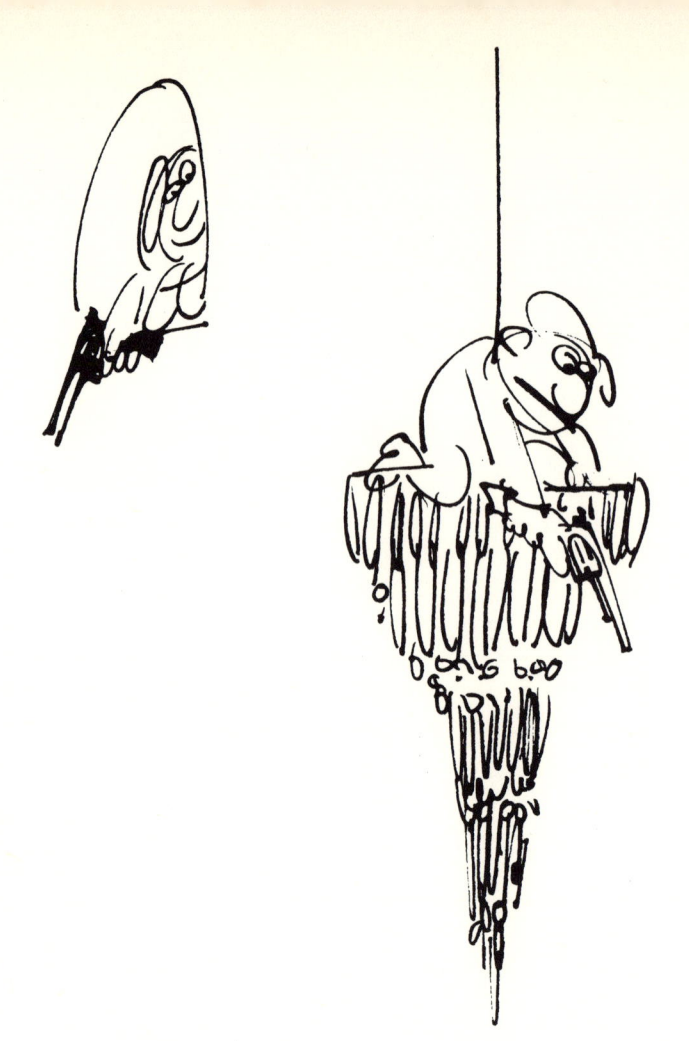

A. G. Sens

© 1969 Sens

Chon Day

"Everyone in Accounting chipped in for the flowers, Mr. Griswold, except Miss Harris, who says she hopes you break your other leg."

Copr. © 1968 The New Yorker Magazine, Inc.

This English nobleman is a tourist at his stately home...

iving a

Good morning, foreign fellow.
You've come to see where it all
began, eh?

Irish are you?

We're thinking of boxing in the bath with hardboard

In the Grand Hall.

we're thinking of having the ceiling lowered with hardboard

...but then in those days we sent them white feathers...

....and

never cared much for painting
myself

not a man's job
I would have thought

bloody artillery was three days late... →

This is the Hunt ballroom and these are working men going about their menial tasks with good humour. We are a fair people and we don't treat our servitors like the animals they are.

...rain stopped play

Prior to moving off to your igloo to impress your peasant family with what you've seen, have you any questions?

Yes. What is this Hardboard?

My God! Don't they have hardboard in AFRICA?

John Glashan

© Glashan

Quentin Blake — "The insects are polythene too, of course." — © Punch 1961

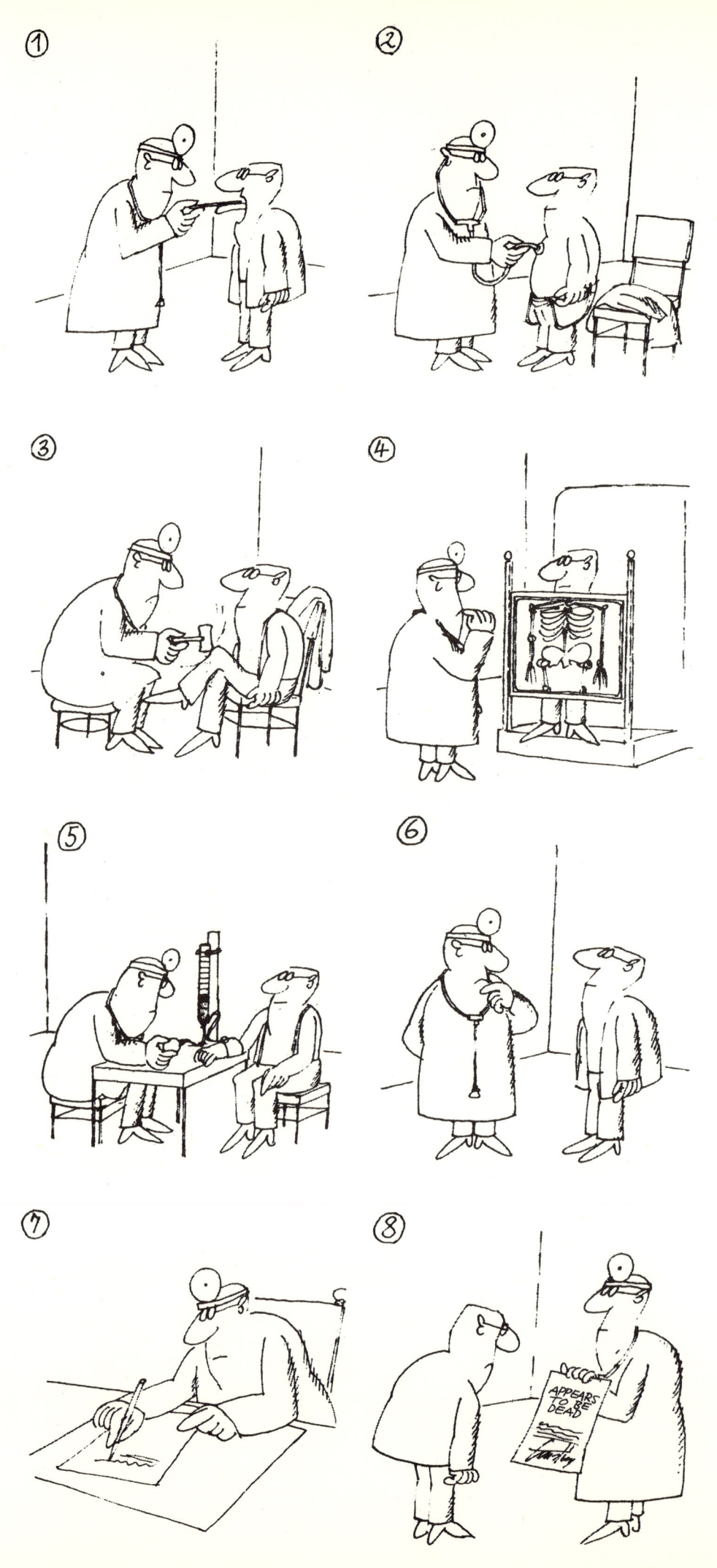

Volker Ernsting

© 1966 Bärmeier & Nikel

Henry Syverson © The Saturday Evening Post

Quentin Blake "That's all the letters, then, Mr. Swinburne—time for your paranoia." © 1969 Blake

William Steig

"Enter Mr. Blotnick."

"Five years! I thought the courts were coddling punks like me!"

Lee Lorenz Copr. © 1968 The New Yorker Magazine, Inc.

Virgil Partch "There are **others**, in case you haven't noticed!" Copr. © 1968 The New Yorker Magazine, Inc.

Eldon Dedini

"Before I begin, I'd like to remind you all that I'm only five years old."

Copr. © 1968 The New Yorker Magazine, Inc.

Guillermo Mordillo

© 1968 Paris Match

Donald Reilly — "Thank you for the marvellous talk, Mr. 46X, and now I hope you'll join us in the Founder's Room for lemonade and cookies."

© 1968 The Curtis Publishing Company
Reprinted with permission from THE SATURDAY EVENING POST.

Lee Lorenz "One adult and one child." © 1966 Look

1

3

Vladimir Renčin

2

4

5

© Dikobraz

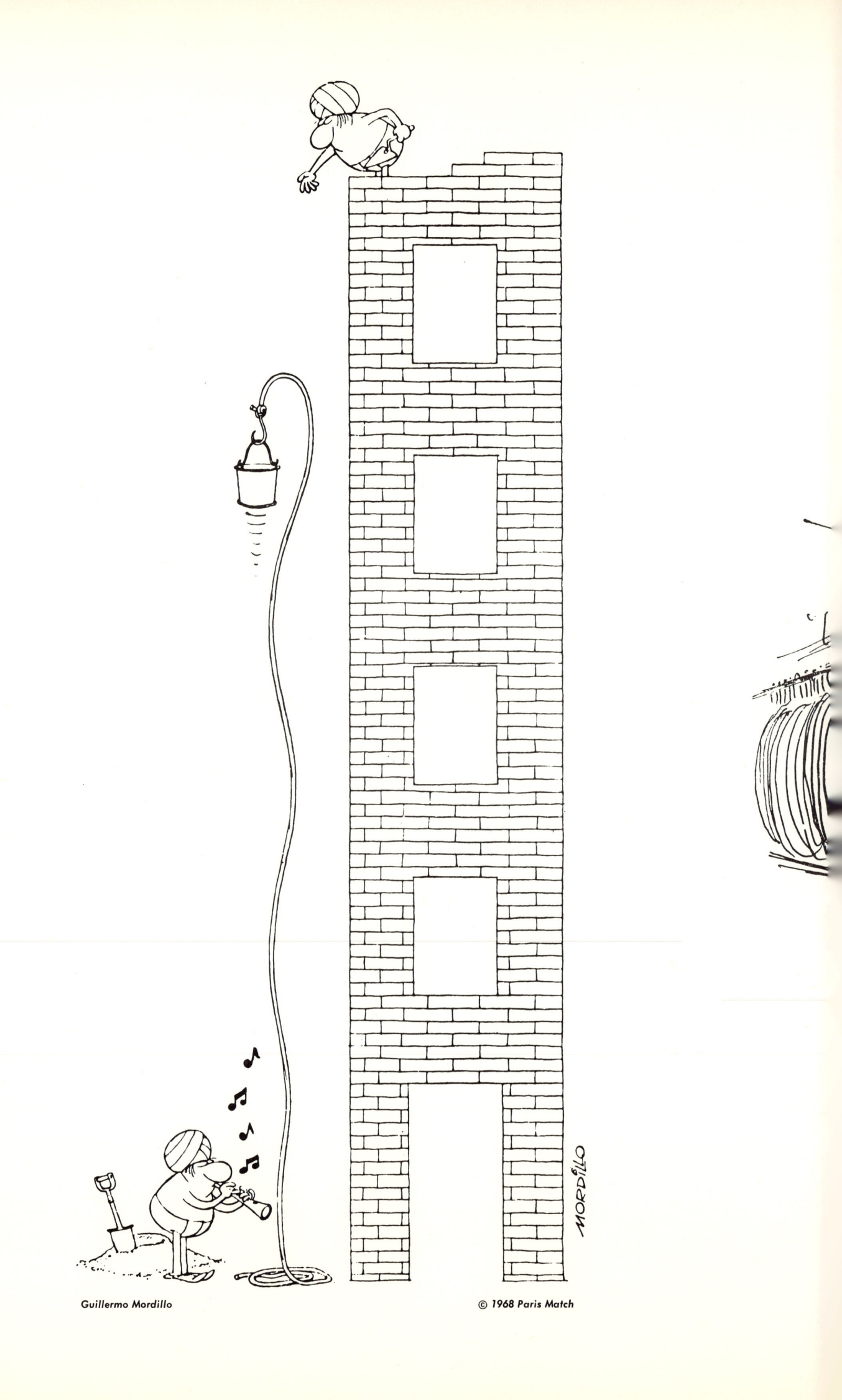

Guillermo Mordillo © 1968 Paris Match

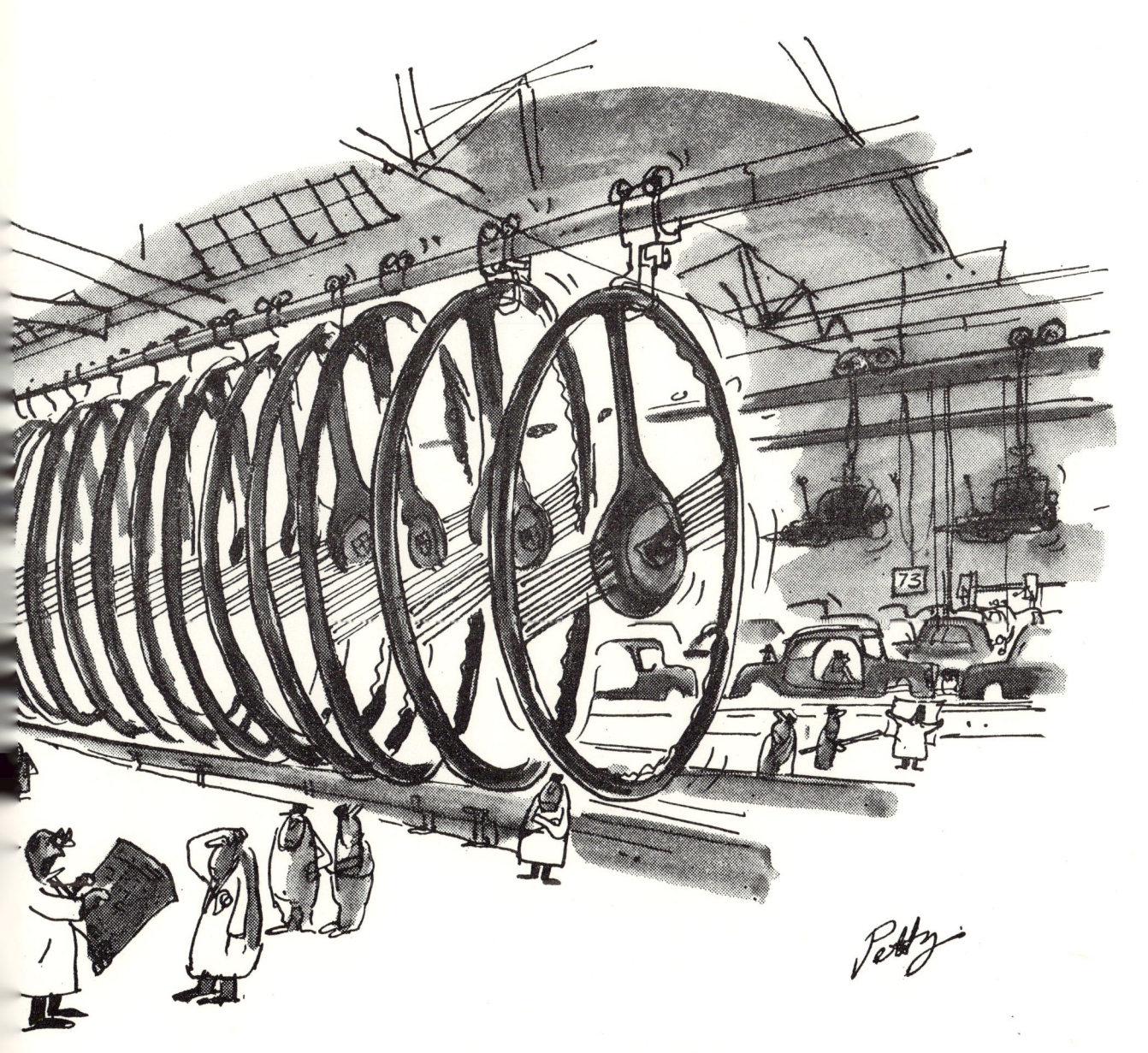

Bruce Petty "Inches, man! Not feet—inches!" © 1965 Punch

Vahan Shirvanian "Scram!" Reprinted with permission from THE SATURDAY EVENING POST.
© 1967 The Curtis Publishing Company

George Price

"Make way for a pedestrian!"

Copr. © 1967 The New Yorker Magazine, Inc.

Terence Parkes

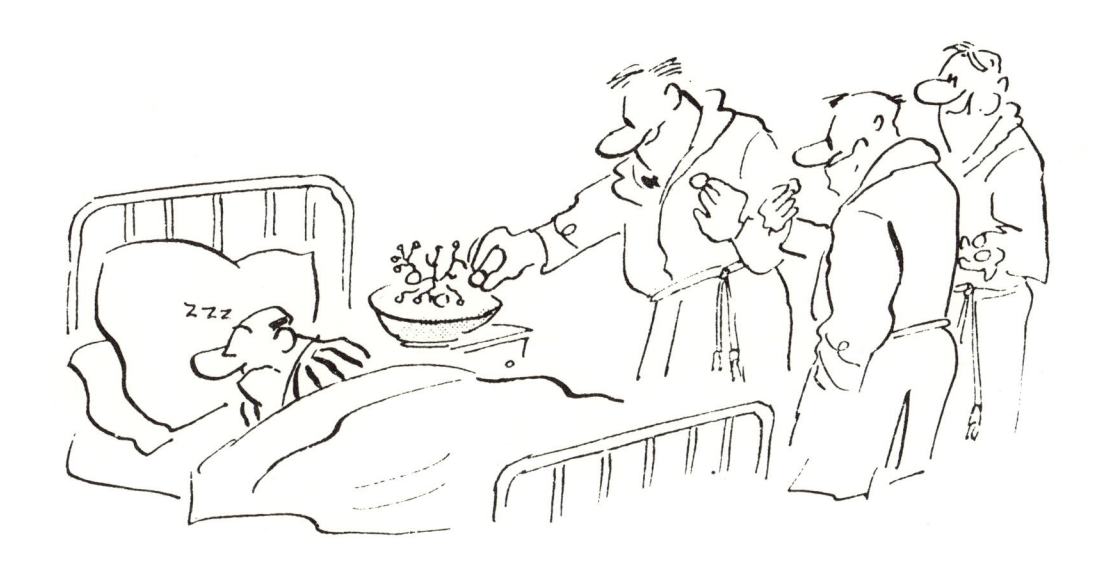

MAN IN HOSPITAL
by LARRY

© 1968 Punch

Stanislav Holý

© Dikobraz

Stanislav Duda © 1969 Duda

Anatol Kovarsky © 1969 Kovarsky

James Stevenson

"This is one of the worst Sundays so far."

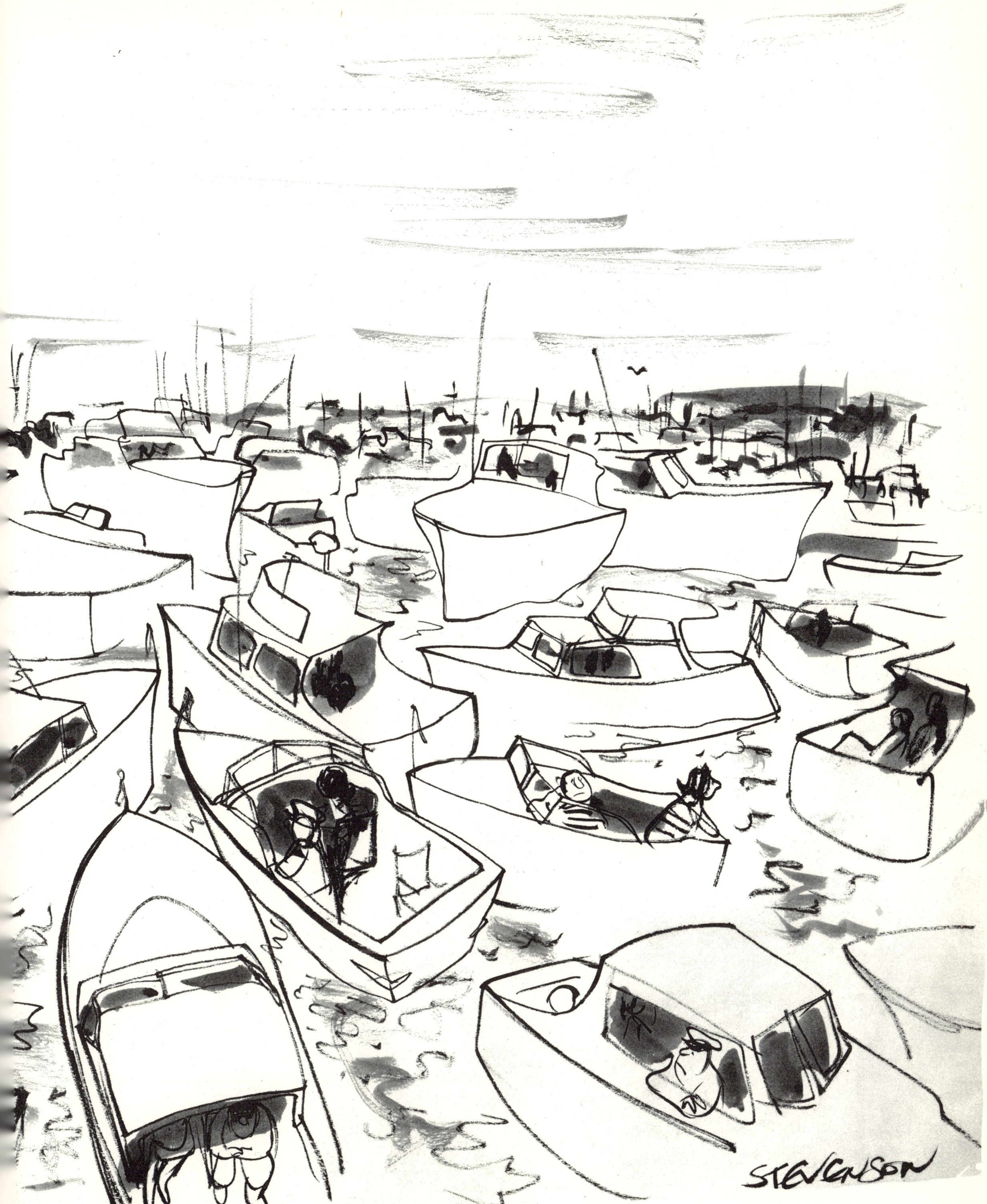
STEVENSON

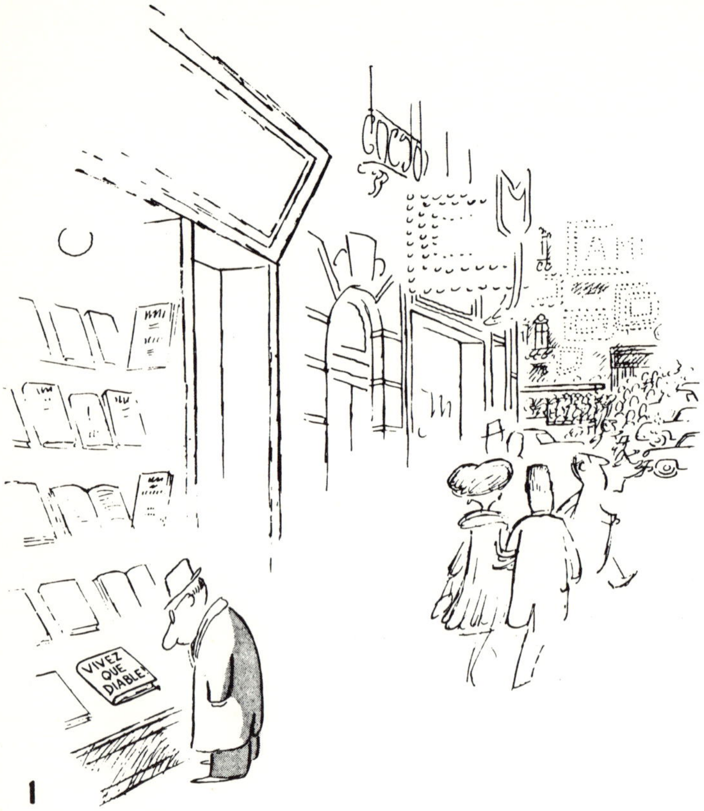

1

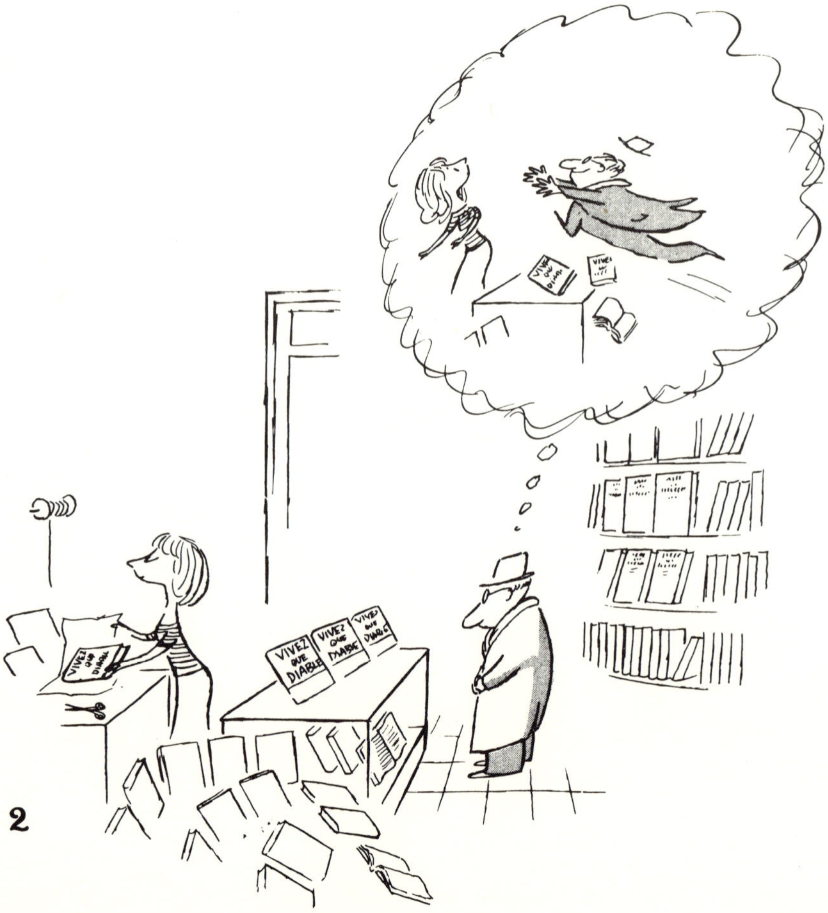

2

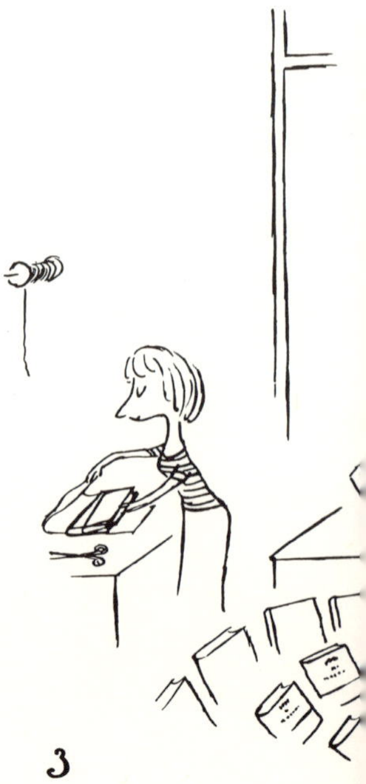
3

5

6

Jean-Jacques Sempé

© by Editions Denoël et Sempé

Robert Day

"Good Heavens, Lydia. Your hair is longer than your skirt!"

© 1967 Saturday Review

Stanislav Holý

© Dikobraz

Bill Tidy "Yes Inspector, those are my husband's feet." © 1967 Punch

Cesc © 1969 Cesc

Cesc

© 1969 Cesc

BOSC

© 1968 Paris Match

"Now he does a little dance, and then she won't be mad."

Charles Saxon

Copr. © 1966 The New Yorker Magazine, Inc.

Anatol Kovarsky

Stan Hunt — "A cup of carrot juice, one poached egg, a slice of toasted protein bread with half a pat of butter, tea with lemon, half a cup of Jell-O, and a goddam vanilla wafer."

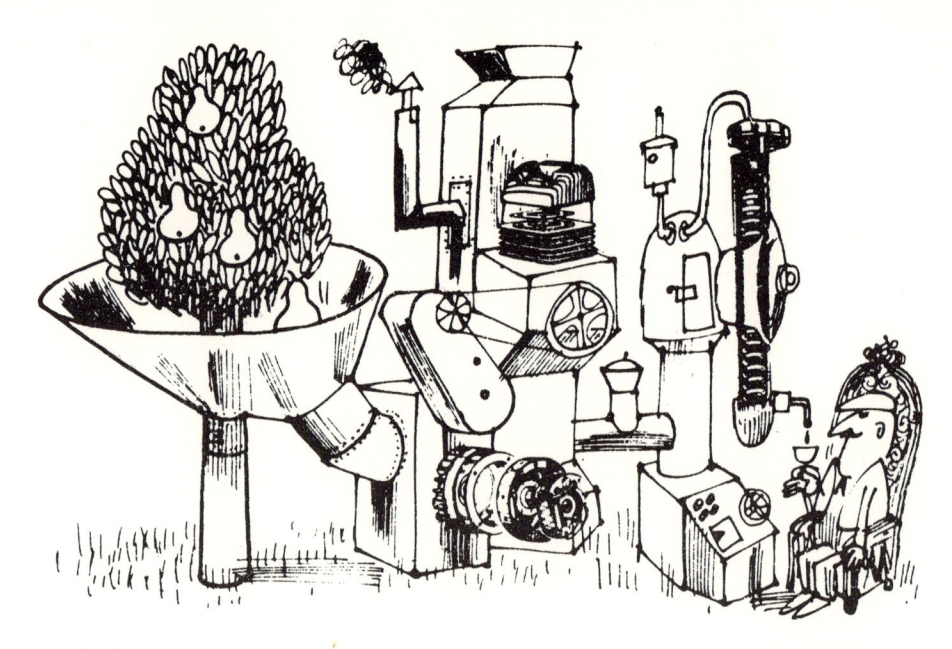

Jules Stauber

© Bärmeier & Nikel

Jules Stauber

© 1968 Stauber

Michael ffolkes

"I'm afraid the bullet holes can be rather draughty."

© 1967 Punch

Mischa Richter

"Seventeen major European cities in twenty-one days."

"That's all I can remember. He had a wart."

Bill Tidy © 1967 Punch

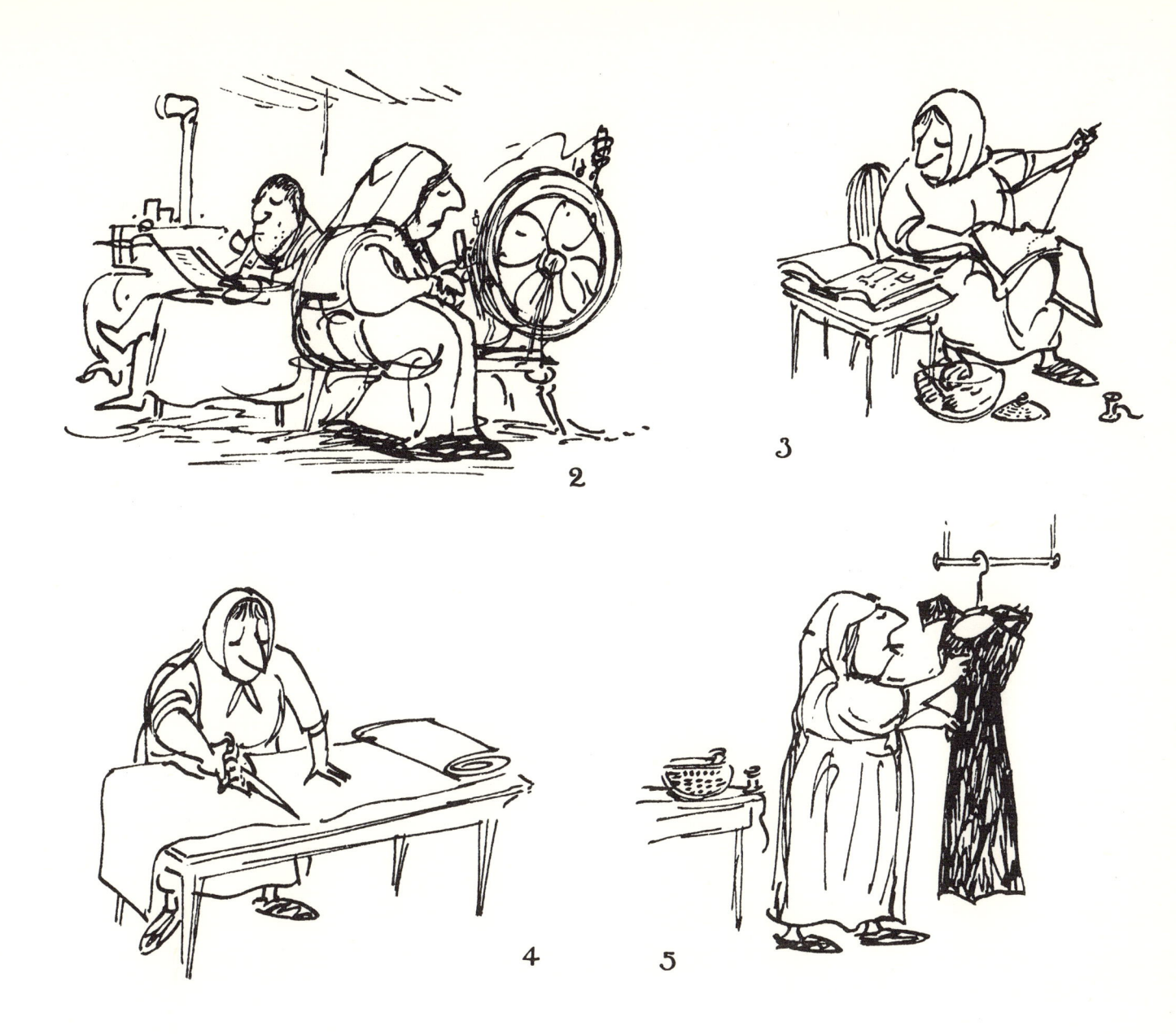

Eldon Dedini

©1969 Eldon Dedini

Leslie Starke

"That's me again on the steps of the what's-its-name."

Copr. © 1969 The New Yorker Magazine, Inc.

"Good God, Alice! This is no time to decide whether our marriage has any meaning! Buzz the door!"

Whitney Darrow, Jr.

Copr. © 1967 The New Yorker Magazine, Inc.

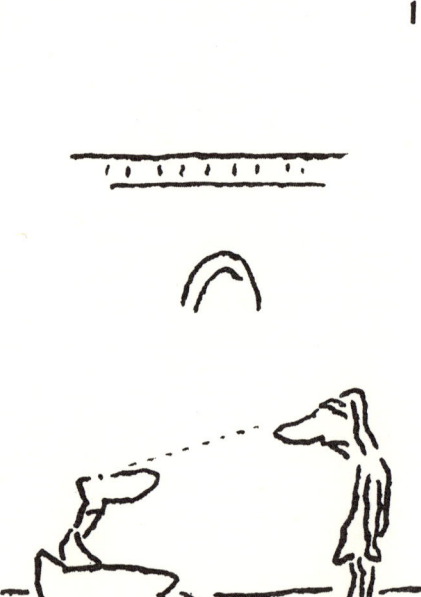

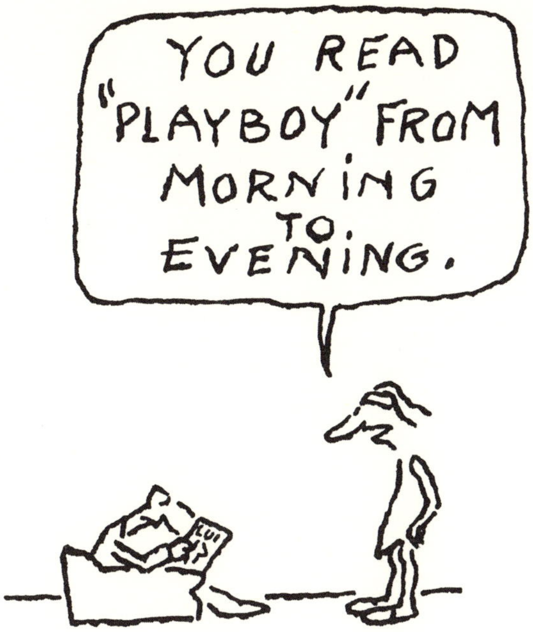

2

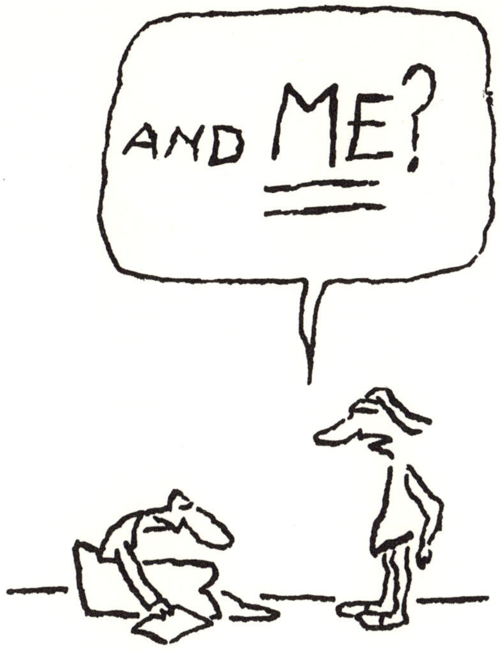

3

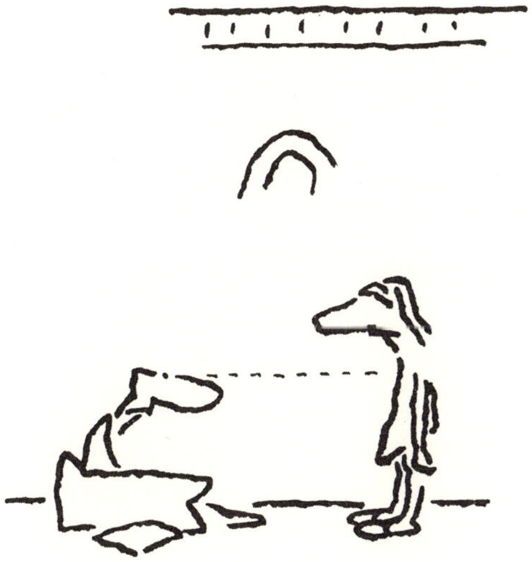

6

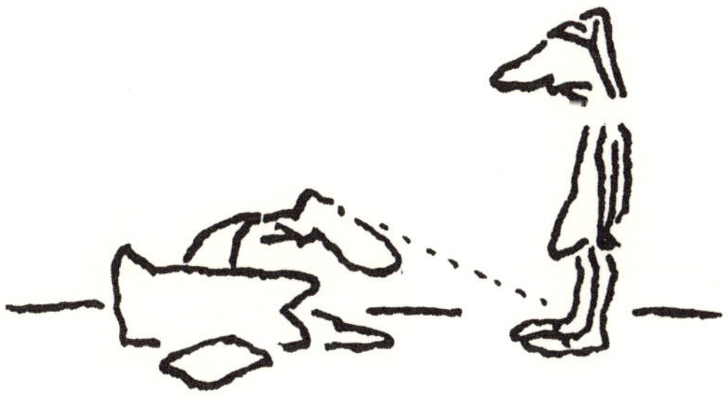

7

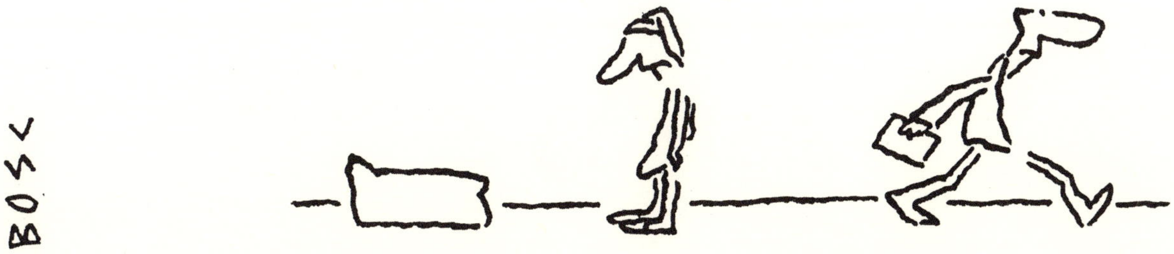

8

Mel Calman

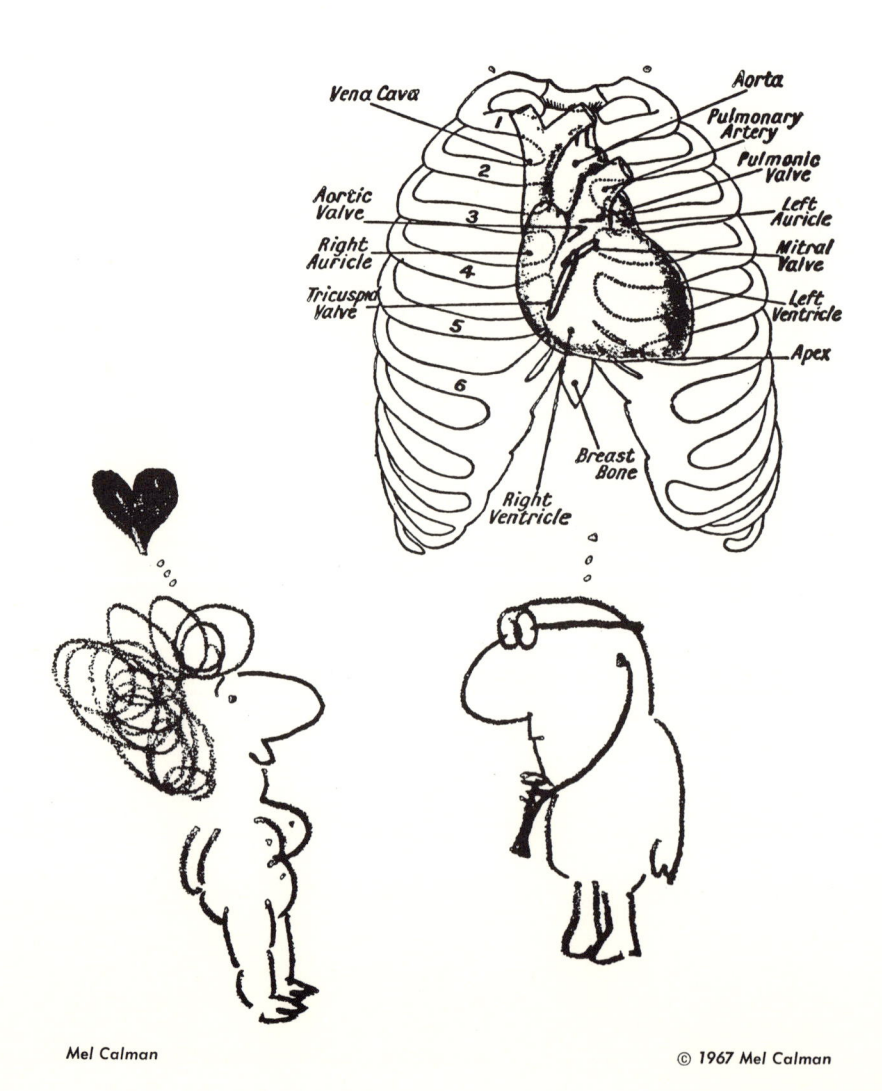

© 1967 Mel Calman

Mel Calman

© 1967 Mel Calman

Charles Martin

"You're complaining! What about me?
I happen to be a very rich man."

Copr. © 1967 The New Yorker Magazine, Inc.

Quentin Blake

1

2

3 4

Barney Tobey — "Never heard of him." — Copr. © 1967 The New Yorker Magazine, Inc.

Vahan Shirvanian

Copr. © 1968 The New Yorker Magazine, Inc.

Claude Smith

3

4

7

© 1967 This Week

Anatol Kovarsky

Harry Hargreaves

© 1969 Kovarsky

HARGREAVES

© 1967 Punch

EXCESS ENERGY

IDÉE FIXE

Lou Myers

DÉJÀ VU

LIBIDO

THE NEUROTICS

GROUP THERAPY

MORBID HUNGER

© Harper & Row

Michael ffolkes

"Somehow I don't think we'll ever know the whole story."

© Punch

PEANUTS featuring "Good ol' Charlie Brown" by Schulz

Charles Schulz

Jean-Jacques Sempé

3

4

5

8

9

12

© by Editions Denoël et Sempé

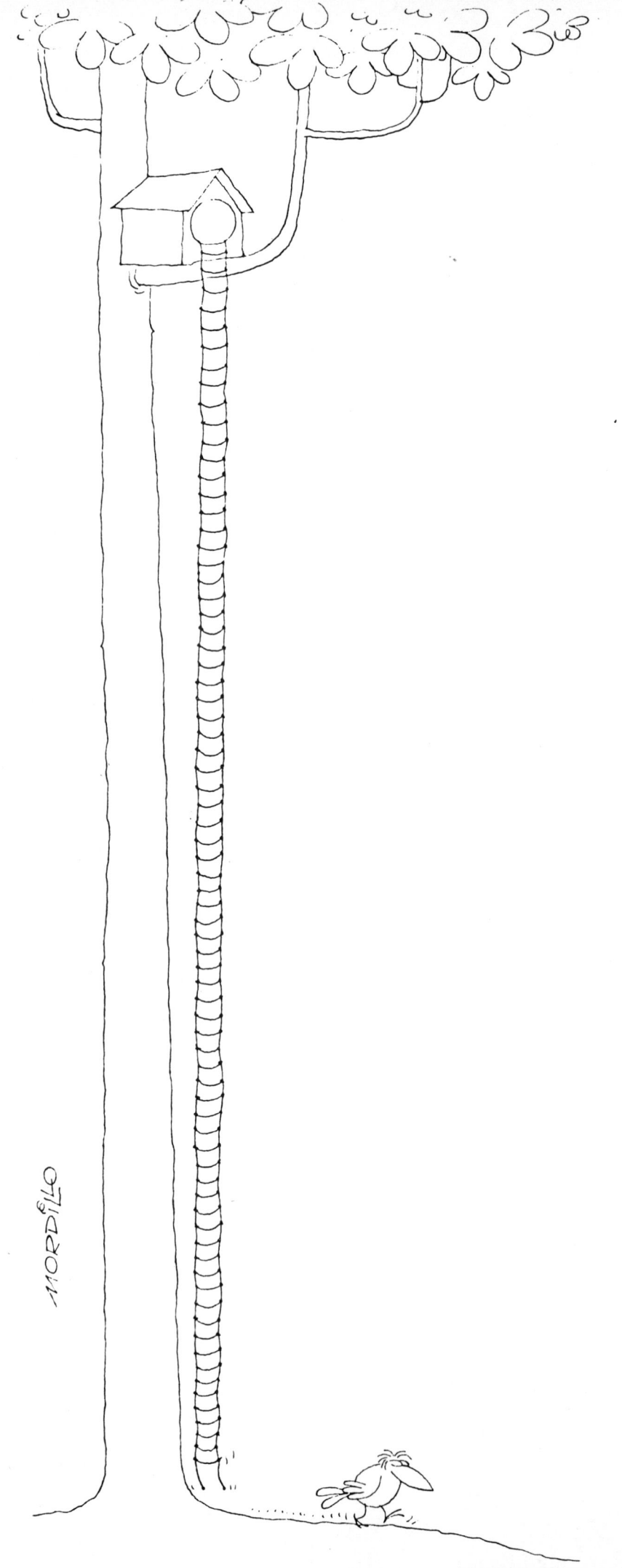

Guillermo Mordillo © 1968 Paris Match